A New Home

Jan Burchett and Sara Vogler
Illustrated by Sarah Nayler

OXFORD

Meg has a home in
a shoe.

The shoe will not do.

Meg gets a new shoe.

The shoe will not do.

Meg gets a new shoe.

The shoe will not do.

Meg gets a new shoe.

The shoe will not do.

Meg gets a big boot.

The boot will do.

Meg has a home in a boot.